Curriculum Foundation Series

ART STORIES
BOOK TWO

By
William G. Whitford
Edna B. Liek and
William S. Gray

Life-Reading Service

SCOTT, FORESMAN AND COMPANY
CHICAGO · ATLANTA · DALLAS · NEW YORK

Grateful acknowledgment is made to the author, John Martin, for permission to reprint the poem "Big Black Bear."

372.5

Printed in the United States of America.

PREFACE

Art Stories, Book Two is the second-grade unit of a group of books devoted to the appreciation of art. This group and similar ones in other subjects make up the Curriculum Foundation Series. Each group of books within the series treats a separate subject, providing suitable content and giving specific training in reading this type of material.

Art Stories, Book Two provides an opportunity to develop in the child an appreciation of beauty. In language suited to the second grade, a number of simple art concepts are presented. Through pictures and story material the child is made increasingly conscious of beauty of color, form, and line as seen in nature, in pictures, in all his surroundings. Elementary ideas of drawing, painting, design, sculpture, architecture, interior decoration, and costume are thus introduced in a setting of natural child interests and activities.

The reading and discussion of such a book will enable pupils to see new beauty in the familiar things of life and will arouse in them an interest in many forms of art.

The illustrations are a special feature of this book. They range from simple line drawings to full-color reproductions of famous paintings and form an integral part of the teaching material. They furnish carefully organized and graded examples of visual material for the teaching of art.

Art Stories, Book Two has been painstakingly edited with regard to reading difficulties—especially in sentence structure and the introduction and repetition of words. The vocabulary is correlated with that of The Elson Basic Readers for the first two grades, as explained on page 164, but *Art Stories, Book Two* may be read without difficulty by any average second-grade group.

STORIES

ANIMALS IN ART (*continued*) PAGE

HOUSES AND YARDS

PICTURES OF THE NORTH AND SOUTH

BEAUTIFUL ROOMS

PICTURES

A number of the pictures in this book are reproductions of paintings, etchings, photographs, or illustrative work that has previously been published. To the owners of these works or of the copyrights we are deeply grateful. The list follows.

The remaining pictures are by the following well-known illustrators of children's books: Pauline B. Adams, Helen Hudson Below, Clarence Biers, Donn P. Crane, L. Kate Deal, Mildred Lyon Hetherington, Miriam Story Hurford, Alexander Key, James McCracken, Electra Papadopoulos, Keith Ward, and Milo Winter.

Part I

Color Secrets

One day the children at school made Easter baskets for their mothers. Miss Long helped them.

"How pretty these baskets are!" said Helen.

"I see red, yellow, blue, green, orange, and violet. There are baskets of all the rainbow colors."

"What can we put in our baskets?" asked Rose.

Bobby said, "Last year I had candy in my Easter basket. Sometimes baskets have flowers in them, too."

Then Barbara said, "Eggs are best for Easter. I think a colored egg would look pretty in each basket."

"Oh, yes!" the children cried. "Let's all put eggs in our baskets."

"Wouldn't it be fun to color the eggs ourselves?" said Rose.

John asked, "May we color them at school?"

"Yes," said Miss Long. "You may each ask your mother to boil an egg for you. Then bring it to school, and I will show you how to color it."

The next day the children all brought eggs to school. On the table they saw three glasses of colored water.

"There is dye in these glasses," said Miss Long. "It will color your eggs.

"You may each make your egg some color of the rainbow."

Bobby colored his egg red. Barbara and Rose made their eggs yellow. Dick colored his egg blue.

Helen looked at the dye and said, "I see only three glasses of dye, and there are six rainbow colors. Where are the other colors?"

Miss Long said, "That is a secret. What color do you want to make your egg?"

"I want to make it green," answered Helen.

Miss Long took a clean glass and put some yellow dye in it. She said, "Now put some blue dye in the yellow."

Helen did as Miss Long told her.

"Oh, it is turning green!" she cried. "Yellow and blue make green. That is the secret."

Helen colored her egg a pretty green.

John mixed a little red dye with some of the yellow and made orange.

Bobby mixed red and blue.

"Oh!" he cried. "Red and blue make violet. Now we have the six rainbow colors."

All the children colored their eggs and put them in the baskets.

When it was time to go home, John said, "We have found out three color secrets today."

What were the secrets?

A Picture of Zinnias

You may have seen flowers like these growing in a garden. They are called zinnias.

Look at the colors of the flowers in this picture. Most of the zinnias are yellow, orange, and red.

These are the colors that we see in sunshine and in fire. We call them warm colors.

Blue, green, and violet are cool colors. We see them in the sky, the trees, and the water. The artist who painted the picture put cool colors on the vase.

Warm colors and cool colors look well together. Why do the zinnias look so pretty with the vase?

What colors did the artist mix to make the orange zinnias? What colors were mixed to make the green leaves?

Watch for beautiful pictures of flowers on magazine covers.

Mixing Colors

Here are three pans of paints. Water is mixed with these paints when they are used. They are called water colors.

What are the colors in the pans?

Name three other colors that can be made from those in the pans.

If you mix red and yellow, what color will you have?

If you mix red and blue, what color will you have?

What colors are mixed to make green?

Can You Find Colors That Match?

When things are the same color, we say they match.

Look at the boy in this picture. There is a basket in front of him. He wants to find an egg that matches it.

Can you find one? Can you find more than one egg that matches his basket?

Look at the girls. Which ones have hair ribbons that match their dresses?

A Color Game

The children in Miss Long's room liked to play a color game. This is the way they played it.

Helen said, "I can see something that matches my book. Guess what it is."

"Is it my dress?" asked Rose.

"Yes," said Helen. "My book is green, and so is your dress."

Then Rose said, "Now it is my turn. I see something that matches my pencil. What is it?"

John said, "Is it that yellow flower?"

Rose laughed and said, "The yellow flower matches the pencil, but I see something else that is yellow."

"Is it that yellow vase?" asked Bobby.

"That is it," said Rose.

Wouldn't you like to play this game?

Ann and the Pink Flowers

Ann was in Grandmother's garden one morning. She was painting a picture.

Grandmother came along and looked at what Ann was doing.

"How do you like this picture?" asked the little girl.

"It is very pretty," said Grandmother. "But you have painted only blue and yellow flowers.

"Many of the flowers in my garden are pink. Couldn't you put some of them in your picture?"

Ann looked at the flowers and shook her head. "There is no pink in my paint box," she answered.

Grandmother said, "Mr. Field is an artist. You might ask him how to paint pink flowers."

So Ann took her paint box and went to see the artist. "I have no pink," she said. "Will you please show me how to paint Grandmother's pink flowers?"

"That is easy," said Mr. Field. "You can make pink by mixing red with white."

He mixed some paint and made a pink flower for Ann.

"Pink is another name for light red," he said. "I will show you how to paint light yellow flowers, too. White mixed with any color makes it lighter."

Ann watched the artist make other light colors. Then he gave her some white paint, and she mixed light colors, too.

Ann asked, "If I mix black with a color, will that make it darker?"

"Try it and see," said Mr. Field.

So Ann mixed a bit of her black paint with some of her red paint. That made dark red. When she mixed black with blue, she made dark blue.

"Thank you," said Ann. "Now I know how to make dark colors and light colors."

Ann went home and painted this picture of Grandmother's pink flowers. She painted some dark green leaves and some light green leaves.

Grandmother liked the picture.

Ann's Gray Kitten

The next day Ann was painting.

She said, "I made pink by mixing red with white. I wonder what I'll have if I mix black with white. I'll try it and see."

So she mixed some black with white.

"Oh!" she cried. "Black and white make gray. Now I will paint a picture of my gray kitten."

Ann made this picture of her kitten.

Light and Dark Colors

Look at the black, white, and gray on this page. Black and white make gray.

Black is darker than gray.

White is lighter than gray.

Look at the colors on the next page. Find light red and dark red.

What is light red called?

Which red has black in it?

Look at the blue colors. Which blue has white in it?

Find all the colors that have white in them.

Find all the colors that have black in them.

Brown is the same as dark orange. Find the brown color.

Tan is the same as light orange. Find the tan color

Courtesy of The Colonial Art Company, Oklahoma City, Oklahoma.

A Spring Dance

This picture shows many of the colors we see in spring.

See the light green leaves on the trees. There are little yellow flowers in the green grass. How bright they look in the spring sunshine!

Far away you can see hills. They have beautiful light colors, too.

There are lovely colors in the clouds. What colors do you see in them?

See the dancers! They are happy because it is spring. All their dresses have very pretty colors. Some are light, and some are dark.

There are many cool colors in this picture.

Can you see blue and violet shadows on the grass? What other cool colors do you see?

Cool colors look better when warm colors are near them.

What warm colors can you find in this picture?

Colors

What is green? The grass is green,
With small flowers between.
What is violet? Clouds are violet
In the summer twilight.
What is orange? Why, an orange,
Just an orange!

Skipping the Rope

Billy, Nancy, and Barbara were good friends. They played together every day.

One spring morning Barbara said, "I have a new skipping rope, and I can skip very fast. Watch me."

Away she went, singing this song.

"Skip, skip, one, two, three.
Who will skip the rope with me?"

Billy and Nancy laughed. "We will skip with you," they cried. "Just wait until we get our skipping ropes."

Soon all three were skipping the rope.

After a while the friends were tired of playing. They went into Nancy's house.

Nancy's mother held up a picture of children skipping the rope. She said, "You made me think of this picture."

The picture is on the next page. Do you like it? It has no rainbow colors, but we can see black and white.

Which children have light hair? Which child has dark hair?

One girl is wearing a dark dress with a design in it. What is the other girl wearing?

See the curved lines of the skipping ropes. What other curved lines can you find in this picture?

A Beautiful Picture

This picture was painted a long time ago.

Its colors are very beautiful. The warm red of the Mother's dress looks pretty with the cool colors of her wrap.

Look at the faces of the Baby and the Mother. Don't you think they are lovely?

What colors do you see on the faces and in the hair?

For many years people have liked to look at this picture. People everywhere know it and love it. That is why it is called a famous picture.

The artist who painted it was named Raphael. He was one of the greatest artists who ever lived. Raphael painted many famous pictures.

This picture of the Mother and Baby is one of Raphael's most famous pictures.

Part II

A Zoo Picnic

A baby elephant had come to live at the zoo. Jim and Barbara wanted to see it.

Mother said, "Let's have a zoo picnic. We will take our lunch and stay all day. Will you help me get the lunch ready?"

"The zoo! The zoo! We are going to the zoo!" sang the happy children, as they helped Mother with the lunch.

As soon as Mother and the children got to the zoo, they went to see the elephants.

"Can the baby elephant eat peanuts?" Jim asked the man with the blue suit.

The man said, "He is too little to eat peanuts, but you may give some to the big elephants."

So Jim bought some peanuts, and the children gave them to the big elephants.

The elephants caught the peanuts one by one and ate them. Just as an elephant ate the last peanut, a big boy came along. He had pictures of the baby elephant.

Barbara said, "You bought the peanuts, Jim. Now it is my turn to buy something. I will get one of these pictures."

Barbara bought a picture, and she and Jim sat down to look at it.

Mother began to take the lunch out of the basket. She gave the children paper napkins. Each napkin had a design of elephants on it.

"These napkins are a nice surprise!" said Jim. "Elephant napkins are just the thing for a zoo picnic."

Barbara began to laugh. She said, "Mother has another surprise. She has brought some animal cookies for our zoo picnic."

After lunch Mother and the children went to see the other animals in the zoo.

They saw bears and tigers. At last they came to the lions. They watched them for a long time.

When it was time to go home, Jim said, "I liked our zoo picnic. I liked the lions."

Barbara said, "I liked the baby elephant best. I'm glad I have a picture of him."

"Wouldn't you like to put it in our basket?" asked Mother.

"Oh, no, thank you, Mother," answered Barbara. "I want to carry it."

Soon Mother and the children were riding along on a street car.

All at once the wind came through the car. It took the picture of the baby elephant right out of Barbara's hand.

Her mother tried to catch it, but she couldn't. The car was going too fast. Barbara's picture flew out of the window.

"Oh, my picture is lost!" she cried.

Mother said, "When we get home, I'll show you an artist's picture of an elephant. If you like it, I'll give it to you."

Barbara began to smile again.

Courtesy of Charles E. Heil.

As soon as they got home, Mother said, "Now we'll look at the picture."

"Oh!" said Barbara. "Isn't it interesting? Some children are feeding peanuts to an elephant.

"We can not see their faces, but their hands show what they are doing."

"The elephant looks happy," said Jim.

"This is an interesting picture," said Mother. "It tells a story with only a few lines.

"Look at the elephant's head. It is just big enough to look well in the space which the artist used. It is not too big for the space, and not too small."

"Mother," said Barbara, "I like this picture better than the one I lost."

"I do, too," said Mother. "We will hang it in your room, Barbara."

Jim said, "When we see this picture, we will think about our zoo picnic."

"Yes," said Barbara. "We'll call it our zoo picture."

"The artist called it Peanuts," said Mother. "Didn't he give the picture a good name!"

An Animal Scrapbook

One afternoon George and Helen and John were having a fine time.

They were looking at old magazines to find animal pictures for their scrapbook.

"Oh, see what I have found in this magazine!" cried John. "It is a tiger."

Courtesy of the New York Zoölogical Society.

Helen said, "I found a colored picture of a tiger, too. Doesn't his fur look pretty!"

John said, "The dark brown lines on the orange fur make a design."

"I am glad we have these tigers for our scrapbook," said George. "Now let me show you what I have found. It is a picture of two bears."

Here is the picture that George found.

These bears are in a tall tree. They seem to be watching something.

An artist made this picture. He likes to paint animals, and he has made many pictures of bears.

This artist used many colors. Look at the black bear. Isn't he a pretty little animal? Do you see the dark colors in his fur?

The brown bear's fur matches the tree back of him. Can you find any other colors in the picture that match?

Name some other colors that you find in this picture.

Look at some magazine covers and see if you can find any other pictures of animals.

If you find some, bring them to school. When you and your friends find enough pictures, you may make a scrapbook.

Reproduced by special permission from *The Saturday Evening Post*, copyright 1930 by The Curtis Publishing Company.

Big Black Bear

A big black bear stood on a ball.
I was afraid that he would fall.
But, no, he didn't fall at all.
He rolled it all around.

I had a ball; I tried to sit
And lie and stand on top of it.
I couldn't do it, not a bit.
I tumbled on the ground.

A Picture of Two Squirrels

Peter was very fond of animals. He had many books with animal pictures in them, and he never grew tired of looking at the pictures.

One day when Peter was looking at a new book, he found a picture of two squirrels.

"What a fine picture this is!" he cried.

He held up the picture and showed it to his mother.

"See the gray squirrels!" he said.

Courtesy of the Earl of Northbrook.

"That is a beautiful picture," said his mother.

"It was made by one of the greatest artists who ever lived. He made it a long time ago."

Peter said, "One squirrel has his long tail curved up over his back. How fluffy his tail is! And aren't the eyes of both squirrels bright!"

"This artist knew how to draw animals," said his mother.

"See how well he showed the squirrels' round backs and funny little ears. And how pretty he made their fur look!"

"The fur looks gray," said Peter.

He looked at the picture again. "I wish I could draw animals," he said.

"Don't be afraid to try," said his mother. "Take your pencil and paper and see what a good squirrel you can make. I will show you how."

She took a pencil and showed Peter how to draw animals with lines.

"This kind of picture is a line drawing," she said. "It is easy to make. You can use both curved and straight lines."

"Oh, I can do that," said Peter.

Soon he had made a drawing of a squirrel.

He showed his drawing to his mother.

"How do you like this picture?" he said. "My squirrel has a fluffy tail, too."

Mother said, "You have made a very good line drawing, Peter."

A Visit to the Art Gallery

The children in Miss Stuart's room went to an art gallery one day. They wanted to see animals that artists had drawn, painted, or modeled.

First they went to a room where there were many drawings made with lines.

"These are line drawings," said Miss Stuart.

"Aren't these pictures drawn with a pencil or crayon?" asked Frank.

"Yes, they are," said Miss Stuart.

The children looked at the drawings and saw many curved lines. There were some straight lines, too.

Frank noticed that each drawing had only a few things in it.

He noticed, too, that the animal in each picture was not too large or too small to look well in the space.

Soon Miss Stuart said, "Now let us look at a few colored pictures."

She took the children to another room.

"Here are some colored pictures that artists have painted," she said.

"See the bears!" cried Mary.

"Look at the bears' fur," said Miss Stuart. "It is a light golden color. The artist used other beautiful colors, too."

"I see blue and violet," said Mary.

Courtesy of The Art Extension Press, Inc., Westport, Connecticut.

"What colors are in the shadows of the bears?" asked Miss Stuart.

Jane said, "I can see blue and violet in the shadows."

Miss Stuart said, "Most of the colors in this picture are light."

"But I see something dark," cried John. "There is brown at the top of the picture."

The children liked the picture of the bears.

"Couldn't we buy it for our school?" asked one of the boys.

"No," said Miss Stuart. "We can't buy the picture, but we can buy a copy of it.

"After an artist has painted a picture, many copies of it can be made. The art gallery has some copies of this picture. They are called prints.

"Anyone can buy a print. We will buy one for our school.

"Come. I will show you some prints."

They went into the next room, and saw some copies of the bear picture.

"The prints look just like the painting," said Bobby. "I am glad we can have a print of the bear picture."

Then the children went into another room. There they saw some animals that artists had modeled.

"These are statues," said Miss Stuart. "Artists make statues of both people and animals."

The children saw statues of elephants, lions, and many other animals.

"Come here," said Miss Stuart. "I want to show you a tiger.

"A great artist made it. An artist who makes statues is called a sculptor."

Courtesy of P. P. Caproni & Brother, Incorporated, Boston, Massachusetts.

"The sculptor put many curves in this statue," said Bobby.

Miss Stuart said, "The tiger's back and tail make a large curve. His legs make curves, too. Isn't it a beautiful statue?"

Jane said, "I wish we could look at these lovely things every day."

"We can look at the bear picture every day," said Frank, with a laugh.

The Little Artists

The children in Miss Stuart's room were talking about their visit to the art gallery.

Betty asked, "Oh, Miss Stuart, couldn't we make an art gallery of our own? We could model lions and tigers, and make drawings and paintings."

Then Mary said, "Couldn't we ask our fathers and mothers to come and see our art gallery?"

"Yes," said Miss Stuart.

All the boys and girls thought it would be fun to have an art gallery at school.

Jack said, "I will make a line drawing of my dog."

Some of the children painted with water colors. A few made colored pictures with their crayons. There were pictures of flowers and trees and animals

After a while Mary said, "Miss Stuart, I am painting a picture. It has many colors in it. See my picture!"

"That is fine," said Miss Stuart.

Some of the children played they were sculptors. They each took some wet clay and rolled it into a ball.

Then they made many different kinds of animals from the clay balls. There were tigers, bears, and lions.

Jack modeled a mother elephant and her baby. The children thought he was the best sculptor of them all.

Miss Stuart and the children put the paintings, drawings, and statues all around the room.

Barbara said, "Now we have an art gallery of our own, haven't we?"

On visiting day the children's fathers and mothers came to see the art gallery. How proud they were!

Pictures and Statues

Turn to the picture of the elephants on page 36. Is it a line drawing?

Look in this book for a line drawing. What page is it on? Can you find other line drawings in this book? Can you find any straight lines in them?

When Frank looked at the drawings made by artists, he noticed two things. What were they? Turn to page 52 to find out if your answer is right.

The children in Miss Stuart's room have a copy of the picture on page 53. What is a copy of a painting called?

If you do not remember, you should read page 54 again.

Name some things you would see if you visited an art gallery.

What kind of work does a sculptor do?

Where have you seen statues?

Part III

A House for Paddy

Paul had played games with Paddy, his new puppy, until he was tired.

"Lie down, Paddy," he said. "Lie down."

He ran to his mother and said, "I wish my puppy could have a house of his own. Couldn't he have a house, Mother?"

"Yes, I think so," said his mother. "We will ask Father."

"I know just how I want the house to look," said Paul.

"Can you draw a picture of it?" asked his mother.

Paul drew a picture that showed the front of a dog house. It had a door in the middle.

"That was easy," said his mother. "Why don't you make a drawing of the side of the house, too?"

So the boy drew another picture. It showed one side of the house.

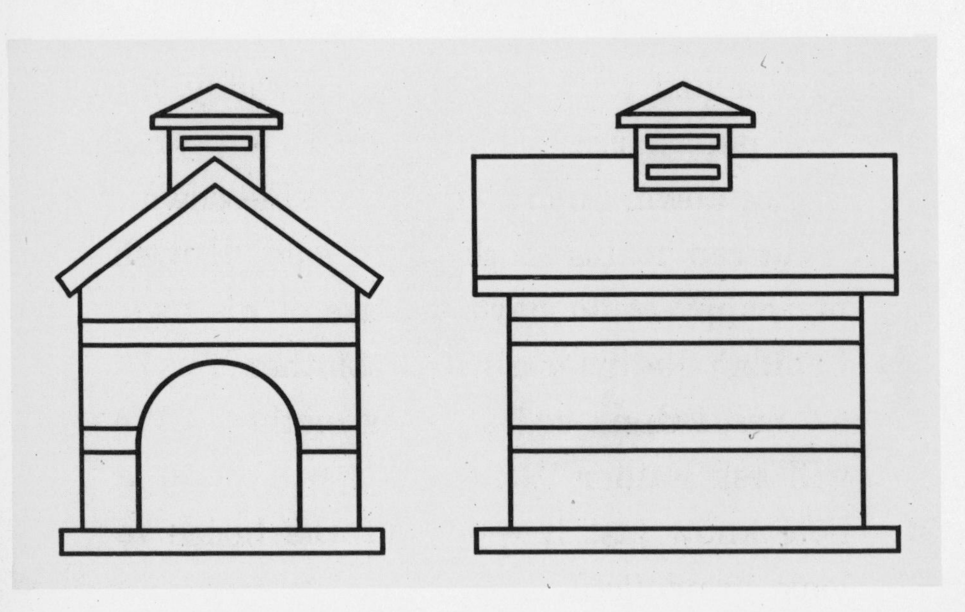

When Father came home, Paul said, "I drew some pictures of a dog house."

"These drawings are fine," said Father. "I am proud of you."

"May Paddy have a house like this?" asked Paul.

"Yes," said Father. "We will build a house for your puppy. It will look like your drawings."

He looked at the drawings again, and said, "I see that you are an architect."

"An architect?" asked Paul. "What is an architect?"

Father answered, "An architect is one kind of artist. He plans buildings. He thinks of the way he wants a building to look. Then he makes drawings of it.

"You have made some drawings that show how you want Paddy's house to look. So I called you an architect."

Then Father began to draw something else.

"My drawing will show the floor of the house," he said. "A drawing that shows the floor of a building is called a plan."

The next day Paul and his father began to build a house for the puppy.

The plan told them just how long and how wide to make the floor of the house and where to put the door.

They sawed some boards and put them together. Soon the walls and roof were built. Paddy's house began to look like Paul's drawings.

While Paul was putting on the roof, Father drew some pictures of the house. Then he painted the house in each picture with different colors.

When the house was almost built, Father gave Paul the colored drawings.

He said, "Paddy's house will soon be done. Then we will paint it. These three pictures will help you choose colors that look well together."

Paul looked at the pictures. Then he said, "I like the light yellow house with the dark green roof and the dark green bands around it."

"Light yellow and dark green look well together," said Father. "Let's see if we can find some paint in my workroom."

"Here is some green paint," said Paul. "But I'm afraid it isn't dark enough."

"We will mix a bit of black with it," said Father. "Then it will be dark green."

Paul found a can of yellow paint, too. He mixed some of it with white to make light yellow.

After Paul had painted the house, his father painted a dog over the door.

"Oh, doesn't that look fine!" cried Paul. "I know Paddy will like the house we have built for him."

"Where shall we put Paddy's house?" Paul asked.

"It will look pretty over there by the bushes and flowers," said Father.

When the paint was dry, they stood the house beside the bushes and flowers.

"Come, Paddy," said Paul. "Your house is built."

The puppy went to the house and sat down in front of the door.

He looked as if he wanted to say, "See my house! I am proud of it."

The Playhouse

One night when Mr. Page came home, Grace and Ruth ran to meet him.

"Oh, Father, Father!" they cried. "May we have a playhouse of our own?"

"Yes," said Mr. Page. "Can you draw a picture to show me the kind of playhouse you want?"

"That will be easy," said Grace. "One day at school we drew plans of houses."

At once Grace began to draw plans for the playhouse.

"How many rooms may we have?" she asked.

"Wouldn't two be enough?" said Father.

"Yes," answered Ruth. "We could have a living room and a kitchen."

Grace said, "I will make the kitchen smaller than the living room."

She drew a plan. It showed the two rooms. Her plan showed where the doors and windows and the chimney should be.

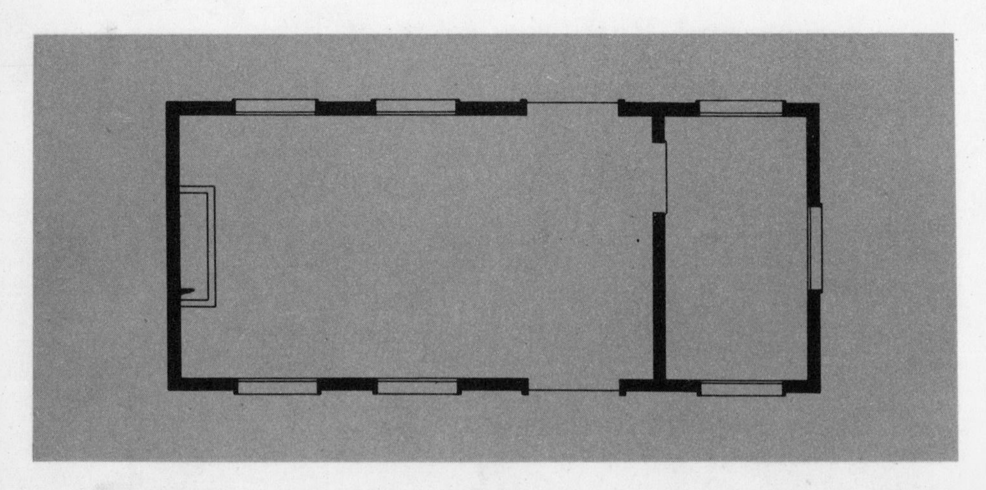

When the plan was made, Grace and Ruth showed it to their father. He said that it was very good.

The next day Mother said, "Haven't you some cardboard? You might make a toy house. It would show how you want the outside of your playhouse to look."

"Oh, yes!" cried Ruth. "Won't you help us make a cardboard house, Mother?"

Mother was glad to help the girls.

They made a pretty little cardboard house with white walls and a red roof. There were windows and doors in the house. It had a red chimney, too.

Mother asked, "Wouldn't you like to put some toy trees and flowers around your house?"

"Oh, yes!" said Grace. "We will make it look as beautiful as we can."

Grace put trees and bushes around the house. Ruth put bright flowers beside it.

When Mr. Page came home, Grace and Ruth showed him the cardboard house they had made.

How surprised he was!

"Doesn't this look fine!" he said. "I will have some men build a house like this for you.

"Your plan and the cardboard house will show them how you want it to look."

After the men had built the house, Father planted a few bushes around it. The girls planted flowers.

Ruth said, "How nice our playhouse looks! It is just like our cardboard house."

"Doesn't it look beautiful with the flowers around it?" said Grace.

"What good times we shall have! We can play games in our playhouse, and we can bring our company here."

Company

My playhouse always is the place
  Where I have company.
For when my friends have said good-by,
  And I'm alone, you see,
The flowers round my playhouse door
  Still smile and bow to me.

Making a House Look Better

Once there was a house that no one lived in. It did not have a pretty, green yard, and there were no flowers or bushes around it.

But a man bought the house.

He said, "This is my house now. I will make it look better."

Notice the two pictures. Tell what the man did to make the house look better.

Courtesy of The Art Extension Press, Inc., Westport, Connecticut.

A Park in the City

The picture on this page shows a park in a big city.

What a pretty place it is!

Parks like this help to make a city beautiful.

The park has green grass and big trees in it.

In the picture there are some tall buildings. They almost seem to reach the sky.

Notice the building near the middle of this picture. What a golden color it has in the sunshine!

The artist has painted some lovely trees in this picture. They have no leaves, but their dark branches make beautiful curved lines.

We see most of the buildings through the trees. Notice the row of low buildings near the park. We see their different colors between the branches.

The curved lines of the trees look pretty with the straight lines of the buildings.

Some of the trees are gray. They look almost like shadows against the light colors of the buildings.

Courtesy of The Art Extension Press, Inc., Westport, Connecticut.

A City Far Away

Some day you may visit the city which is shown in this painting. It is interesting because there are many beautiful buildings there.

But if you never visit the city, you may still enjoy this picture of it.

The artist saw beautiful colors on the roofs of these houses. Some were warm colors, and some were cool.

The colors looked very pretty together. So he put them in the picture.

The sun is low in the sky. Near the street we can see shadows. But the tops of the houses and the chimneys are tall enough to reach the sunlight.

The artist used both light and dark colors. See the windows. Some are light, and some are dark.

Find other light and dark colors in the picture.

Look at the queer roofs and the high chimneys. Don't they make the buildings look tall?

Where did the artist use straight lines in his painting?

Artists have made many pictures of buildings. Look for some of these.

Three Architects

One afternoon John Bush visited his father's workroom. Mr. Bush was an architect who drew plans for buildings.

"May I draw a building, Father?" asked John. "I like to use your drawing board."

His father said, "Yes."

Soon John had made a drawing.

"That is fine," said Mr. Bush. "You have made a house."

John laughed and asked, "How can you tell that it is a house?"

"That is easy," said his father. "It has the form of a house. The form of a building is its shape.

"Look at that drawing on the wall. Can you tell what kind of building it is?"

"It doesn't look at all like the house I drew," said John. "It has a different form. It is an office building, isn't it?"

"Yes," said Mr. Bush. "What do you notice about its form?"

John thought for a little while. Then he said, "The office building is very tall and not very wide."

Just then some men came to see Mr. Bush, and John went home.

At home he found his cousin Billy.

The boys played with John's blocks. They made buildings of different forms. Some were tall, and some were low.

John said, "I like to build. I want to be an architect like Father when I'm big."

"And I'm going to be an architect like my uncle," said Billy.

Architects and Their Work

Do you know what an architect does? If you do not remember, read page 66 again. What else do you know about architects and their work?

Architects are artists. Can you name any other kinds of artists? Tell what work each kind of artist does.

What is an architect's drawing of a floor called? Look at the picture on page 72. How many rooms are shown?

The plan shows three doors and seven windows. Tell where they are.

In the picture on page 68 each house has colors that look well together. What colors does each house have?

Look at the picture on page 77. What was done to make the house look better?

What can we do to make the yards around our homes more beautiful?

Part IV

Outdoor Pictures

Tom and Mary Hill were on the train with their father and mother. They were going to visit their cousins in the South.

It was the middle of winter. In the North, where Tom and Mary lived, the ground was covered with snow.

"Look out of the window, Mary," said Tom. "See the trees over there."

"How pretty they look!" cried Mary.

Mr. Hill said, "Winter in the North is so beautiful that artists often paint pictures of it."

"I don't think they can paint anything as beautiful as this," said Tom.

Mr. Hill said, "I can show you some winter pictures that are more beautiful than what you see from the car window.

"We shall reach a big city early this afternoon, and the train for the South doesn't leave until evening.

"While we are in the city, we will go to the art gallery."

When they reached the art gallery, Father took Mary by the hand. They all went upstairs and walked through some of the rooms without stopping.

Suddenly Tom cried, "I see a picture of the North. People are having fun in the snow. Let's look at that one."

Courtesy of Molly Luce.

They all stopped to see the picture. In it some children were going down a low hill on sleds.

"Oh, see the men on the ice!" cried Mary.

"This picture shows some winter fun," said Tom. "It makes me think of good times we have at home."

They walked along and looked at other pictures. One was a beautiful painting of woods in winter.

"The artist didn't put any people in this picture," said Mary.

"No," answered Mrs. Hill. "He wanted to show the woods in winter and the lovely colors we see outdoors.

"See the golden colors on the trees and the blue shadows on the snow. The artist called the picture Sunlight and Shadow."

Father said, "On the water we see many different colors."

"I like this picture," said Tom. "It is much more beautiful than anything I saw from the car window."

They all laughed.

Mother said, "Your cousins in the South have never seen snow. Let's buy a copy of this painting and take it to them."

So Father bought a print of the picture.

Courtesy of Edward W. Redfield.

Then the Hill family went into another room of the art gallery.

"Here is a famous picture," said Mrs. Hill. "It was painted by an artist named George Inness. It shows a beautiful place in the South.

"Can you see why Mr. Inness called it Early Morning?"

"Oh, yes!" cried Mary. "I think the sun is just coming up."

Mother said, "It makes a lovely rosy light. Aren't the clouds pink!

"The roofs have a warm color in the sunlight. You can see the sunlight on the trees and the ground, too."

Mr. Hill said, "Look at the trees. They have some straight lines and some curved lines.

"You will see trees like these in the South. Their leaves are green all the year round."

Courtesy of The Art Institute of Chicago.

Tom said, "Some of the trees look far away, and some of them seem near us."

"The trees that look far away are in the background of the picture," said Mr. Hill. "The ones that seem near us are in the foreground. What else do you see in the foreground?"

"I see a man standing alone," said Mary. "There is a bridge, too."

Mother said, "Inness put dark shadows in the foreground. He painted light colors in the background.

"Inness made many beautiful pictures of different places."

Tom said, "Father, I like this picture. Won't you buy a copy of it? Then we can enjoy it at home."

"Yes," said Mr. Hill. "We bought a picture of the North for your cousins. We will buy a copy of this picture of the South for ourselves."

Blue Johnny

The next afternoon the Hill family reached the town where Uncle Ned lived. He had come to meet the train.

When the train stopped, Tom got off first. "Hello, Uncle Ned!" he cried.

They all got into Uncle Ned's car and started for his house.

"Peter and Ann can't wait for their cousins to come," said Uncle Ned. "They want you to see Blue Johnny."

"Who is Blue Johnny?" asked Tom.

"You will soon see," said Uncle Ned.

The children began to wonder what they would see at Uncle Ned's.

But they were both busy looking out of the windows of their uncle's car, and they did not remember about Blue Johnny very long.

While they were riding along the wide streets, they noticed beautiful trees and bright flowers.

After a while the car stopped in front of a pretty house.

"Here we are," said Uncle Ned.

Aunt Molly, Peter, and Ann were there. Everyone laughed and talked about the trip on the train.

Suddenly Tom saw Peter's blue wagon standing near by, and he remembered what Uncle Ned had said.

"Oh!" he cried. "Is that Blue Johnny?"

Peter laughed, and Ann said, "No, that is not Blue Johnny. Come with us, and we will show him to you."

The four cousins went to the garden. There they saw a pool with flowers in it. Something else was in the pool, too.

"Oh!" cried Mary. "Blue Johnny is a funny big bird. Where did you get him?"

Peter said, "When he was just a little bird, Father found him in the woods and brought him to us. We named him Blue Johnny."

"Now he lives in our pool," said Ann. "But when he was small, he lived near a big pool that had trees around it."

"Father says that one of our pictures looks almost like Blue Johnny's first home," said Peter. "Don't you want to see the picture?"

"Oh, yes!" cried Tom and Mary.

So the children went into the house to look at the painting. Their mothers and fathers looked at it, too.

"I like the colors in this picture," said Mrs. Hill.

Mr. Hill said, "The artist must have enjoyed painting these big trees. What beautiful curves the branches have! This is a lovely picture."

Courtesy of Marie A. Hull.

Mary said, "If Blue Johnny's first home looks like this picture, it must be a very pretty place."

"You will see many lovely places in the South," said Aunt Molly.

Just then the children heard a queer noise coming from the garden.

"What is that?" asked Tom.

"Blue Johnny is hungry," said Ann.

"Can't we feed him?" asked Mary.

So the four cousins went back to the garden.

Ann gave some pieces of bread to Blue Johnny, and he ate them. He even came up and ate out of her hand, while the other children watched him.

Beauty Out of Doors

In every part of our country there are beautiful things to see.

In the North, where Tom and Mary live, you can see the beauty of snow and ice in the winter. You can see trees and flowers and birds in the summer.

In the South, where Peter and Ann live, you can see lovely flowers and trees and birds all the year round.

What beautiful things do you see in your part of the country? When you look around, can you see hills and wide fields and clouds?

Or do you see buildings with different forms?

Artists have made many pictures of beautiful places.

Almost everyone enjoys a fine picture. Tell about a picture that you like.

Part V

Playrooms

Mr. King had just bought a house. It was old, but the rooms had been papered and painted, so that they looked like new.

When the family were almost ready to move into the house, Mother took Ray and Alice to see it.

"I have a surprise for you," she said. "Come upstairs with me."

Mother and the children went upstairs. There they saw two low rooms with a door between them.

“What are these rooms for?” asked Ray.

“I thought you might have them for playrooms,” said Mother. “Some new paint will make them look pretty.”

“Won’t it be fun to have playrooms for ourselves!” said Alice. “We can have a living room and a dining room here.”

Ray asked, “May we paint the walls ourselves?”

"Yes," said Mother. "But before you begin to paint, we must think about what you are going to put in each room.

"The color of the walls must look well with the carpet, curtains, and furniture."

Then Mrs. King showed the children some pictures of beautiful rooms.

She said, "See this picture. How well the walls and carpet look together.

"What do you notice about the light and dark colors in these rooms?"

Ray looked at the pictures again and said, "Aren't almost all the ceilings lighter than the walls?"

"And the walls are lighter than the floors," said Alice.

"Yes," said Mrs. King. "In many rooms the colors are lighter at the top."

Then the children began to plan their living room.

"We have a brown carpet that you may use," said Mother. "What colors will look well with the carpet?"

"I should like tan walls and a lighter ceiling," said Ray.

"I should like orange curtains," said Alice. "Won't orange curtains look well with tan and brown?"

"Yes," said Mother. "These three colors look well together. But tan and brown and orange are all warm colors. Your room will need some cool colors, too.

"Usually a room looks better when it has both warm and cool colors. What cool colors will you have?"

"Some of our books are blue and green," said Ray. "And we can get a blue vase."

"Your living room will look well," said Mother. "Now let's plan the dining room."

"Let's paint the walls and ceiling with warm colors, like those we are going to have in our living room," said Ray.

"We can put a dark blue carpet on the floor. Then the room will have both warm and cool colors."

Mother smiled and said, "You didn't forget the cool colors this time, did you, Ray?"

Alice was glad that Ray wanted a blue carpet, because she was fond of blue.

"Can't we have blue furniture, too?" she asked.

"Yes," said Mother. "Blue furniture and a blue carpet will look well together. But you will need more warm colors.

"You might have curtains with yellow in them. Then you could have some dishes with warm colors."

"I should like some orange-colored dishes," said Alice.

That evening the children told Father all about their plans for the playrooms.

He said, "Very well. We'll begin to paint the walls tomorrow."

The next day Father bought the paint. The children painted the part of the walls they could reach. Mr. King painted the walls higher up and the ceilings.

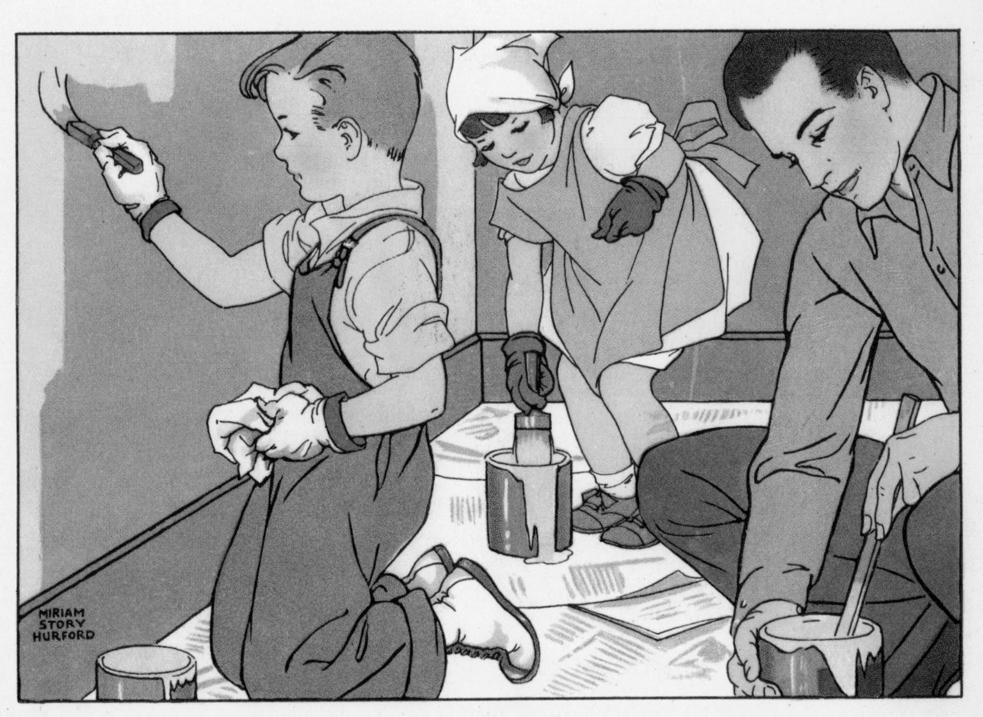

As soon as the carpets and furniture were in their places, Mother helped Ray and Alice hang the curtains.

While the family were all at work, a boy brought a big package. Some pretty orange-colored dishes were in it.

"Aren't they lovely!" cried Alice.

"I will put them on the cupboard shelves. Their warm color will look well in our dining room. The dishes will make the room even more beautiful than it is now."

Surprise Packages

One evening Mr. King came home with two big packages.

"Guess what I bought for you today," he said to Ray and Alice.

The children tried to guess from the shape of the packages.

At last Father said, "The things that I bought were made by artists. Now can't you guess?"

"I know!" cried Alice. "Haven't you some pictures for our playrooms?"

"Yes," said Father. "I want to see how you like them."

Courtesy of The Art Institute of Chicago.

He held up a picture of some geese.

"Don't the geese look pretty in the flower garden!" cried Alice. "They have found a good place to take a walk."

"Yes," said Father. "Even geese seem to be fond of flower gardens."

"I like this picture," said Ray. "It makes me think of our garden on a summer morning."

"It is a pretty picture," said Mother. "Do you want to hang it in your living room or your dining room?"

Alice looked at the picture for some time. Then she said, "The warm colors in this picture are light. So we notice the cool colors more.

"Our living room needs cool colors. I think the picture of geese and flowers will look better in the living room than in the dining room. Don't you, Ray?"

"Yes, Alice, you are right," said Ray. "The cool colors will be pretty in our living room."

The children helped Father hang the picture of the geese in the living room.

"This picture is just what you needed here," said Mother.

Then Mr. King opened the other package and held up a picture of sunflowers.

"I wonder if you will like this picture for your dining room," he said. "It is a copy of a painting, too."

"Oh!" cried Alice. "The sunflowers look as warm and bright as sunshine."

Ray said, "Our dining room needs more warm colors. Most of the colors in this picture are warm. It will look well in the dining room."

Mother said, "The artist made the flowers large, so that they would look well in the large picture.

"The sunflowers all have golden colors. There are golden colors on the table and the vase, too. The cool background makes the golden colors look beautiful."

"Wouldn't the space between the door and the cupboard be a good place for the picture?" asked Father.

Courtesy of The Colonial Art Company, Oklahoma City, Oklahoma.

"The picture is just large enough to look well in that space," said Mother.

They hung the sunflower picture in the dining room between the cupboard and the door.

Its warm golden colors looked lovely with the colors of the room.

"A beautiful picture helps make a room look well," said Father.

"The picture looks better here than it did in the store."

"And the room looks better than it did before we hung the picture," said Alice.

Ray said, "The artists who painted our new pictures have helped make our rooms beautiful. Now we are ready for company."

What Alice Found Out

One morning Alice was alone upstairs in the playrooms. She had just cleaned the living room.

"This room looks nice now, because it is neat and clean," she said.

"But I'm tired of seeing the pieces of furniture in the same places every day. I think I will change them around."

So she moved the chairs and tables to different places.

Suddenly Ray came running into the living room.

He ran into a chair in the middle of the room and tumbled over it.

"Alice!" he said. "Why did you change the furniture around?

"Why was this chair standing in the middle of the room? It usually is beside the wall."

Ray looked around, and then he laughed and laughed.

"Oh, dear, how funny our living room looks!" he said.

"The furniture is all on one side of the room."

Alice laughed, too.

She said, "I moved the pieces of furniture because I wanted the room to look different."

"Shall we try to make the room look better?" asked Ray. "We won't put all the big pieces on one side of the room."

"All right," said his sister. "But let's change things so that the room will look different from the way it was."

Ray said, "We might begin by leaving a place for people to walk. Then they won't tumble over chairs and tables."

The children moved all the pieces of furniture. When they were through, one side of the room looked like this.

They made another side of the room look like this.

When the moving was done, Ray said, “Doesn’t this room look better now?”

“Yes,” said Alice. “The next time I change our furniture around, I’ll try to make it look well.”

Why did the living room look better after Ray and Alice changed it?

Different Kinds of Designs

Designs are used to make things pretty.

Look at this picture of the playroom cupboard. Alice has put some paper on the cupboard shelves. The paper has a design on it.

This design shows the same thing over and over. It shows a row of geese, one after. the other.

Look at the design at the top of this page. Different things are shown in it.

First you see a bird and then a squirrel. You see a row of birds and squirrels, one after the other.

Look at the other design on this page. Does it show different things, or does it show the same thing over and over?

Here is another interesting design. It has a row of light and dark leaves. The first leaf is light green, and the next one is dark green.

A design with only one row of things is called a border design. You often see designs of this kind.

Other designs have many rows. They are called all-over designs.

Look at the picture on page 116. There is an all-over design on the curtains. Why is it called an all-over design?

You can see all-over designs on clothes, too. Look through this book and find some pictures of clothes with all-over designs.

Can you find any other all-over designs in the pictures of this book? Can you find some border designs in it?

Here is a picture of some wall paper. Does it have an all-over design or a border design?

Notice the designs on the wall paper that you see.

Can you think of any other things that have all-over designs?

A Picture of a Room

Many years ago a great artist lived in a country far away. He liked to paint pictures of people in their homes.

This artist has been called a painter of sunshine, because he loved to paint sunlight shining into a room. He liked to show the sunshine falling on people.

Here is one of his pictures. In it we see a large room. A woman and a little girl are standing between two open doorways.

One doorway opens into a darker room. But there is a low window that lets in a bit of light.

Through the doorway on the right we can see another room. It is bright with sunshine.

The light shines on the child. You can see the golden colors of her hair.

Courtesy of The Colonial Art Company, Oklahoma City, Oklahoma.

Look at the child's dress. What colors do you see on it?

What colors do you see on the woman's dress?

There are many warm colors in the room. How many can you name? What cool colors do you see?

The ceiling is a beautiful brown. Can you find dark brown and light brown in the picture?

We can not see any furniture in the large room. Where in the picture do you see a piece of furniture?

The floor of the large room has a design. Is it an all-over design or a border design?

What colors do you see in this design?

Why do these two colors look well together?

This is a famous picture. Why do you think people like it?

Beautiful Rooms at Home

Would you like to help Mother make your home look pretty?

Here are some things to remember.

A room looks well when it is clean and neat. After you have used something, you should put it back in its place.

Every room should have colors that look well together. A room needs some cool colors and some warm colors.

Pictures help make a room beautiful. They should have colors that look well in the room.

The pictures should not be too large or too small for the wall space. They should not be hung so high that people have to look up to see them.

On what pages does your art book show designs in curtains or wall paper? Look in your home for designs, too.

Part VI

Prince Carlos and His Pony

Once there was a little boy who was called Prince Carlos. His father was the king of a great country.

The king was fond of horses and liked to ride in the woods and fields.

When Prince Carlos was only a little boy, the king gave him a pony.

The prince was not afraid, and soon he was a good rider. The king was proud of him.

Then the boy and his father often went riding together. What good times they both had!

One day the king said, "I should like to have a picture of the prince riding on his pony."

The king sent for a friend who was a great artist and asked him to paint a picture of the prince.

Courtesy of The Art Extension Press, Inc., Westport, Connecticut.

The artist made this picture of Prince Carlos when the boy was seven years old. It is a famous painting.

See how the prince is galloping along on his pony. How straight he is sitting! Doesn't he look proud?

The artist used warm colors to paint the child and the pony. He painted a background of cool colors to make the warm colors look brighter.

This artist made many pictures of the king and his family. He liked to paint them in beautiful clothes.

Notice the colors in the picture of Prince Carlos. He has a large brown hat, and his suit has golden colors.

Name some colors the artist painted in the background.

Look at the foreground. What colors did he use on the horse and on the boy's clothes?

Bonnie's Party

When Bonnie was seven years old, she had a birthday party. Seven girls and seven boys came. They wore their best dresses and suits.

After a while Bonnie gave each boy a colored balloon and each girl a doll on a stick. The dolls were dressed in different colors.

She said, "Now we are going to march by twos, and you must each find the one who is to march with you.

"Each boy may find a girl who has a doll that matches his balloon."

What fun the children had matching their dolls and balloons! Then two by two they marched around the yard.

"This is like a parade," said Joe.

Then the children all marched to the dining room and found their chairs. In the middle of the table there was a big birthday cake. Each child had a colored napkin with a border design.

After a while Bonnie's mother said, "We have a surprise for you." She drew back a curtain that hung on the wall.

"Why, it's a picture of Bonnie!" cried Alice. "How lovely it is!"

Betty said, "I wonder why the dress is not like the ones Bonnie usually wears."

"The artist who painted the picture planned the dress for me," said Bonnie. "She wanted clothes that would look like the ones people used to wear long ago."

Bonnie's mother said, "See what lovely colors the artist put in the picture. The red dress looks well against the dark green background."

"Red is a good color for you, Bonnie," said Mary, "because your eyes are dark."

John looked at the picture and said, "The kitten's white fur matches the white on Bonnie's dress."

Just then Fluffy went up to the picture. "Mew, mew," he said.

Alice laughed and said, "Fluffy wants us to notice his picture, too."

Courtesy of Karl S. Bolander.

A Boy of Long Ago

Here is a picture that was painted by a great artist a long time ago.

Perhaps the clothes in this picture seem queer to you. But they are the kind of clothes that little boys usually wore in those days.

See the big black hat. Doesn't it look pretty with the boy's light suit? His blue sash is a lovely color, too.

These colors look well on him, because he has rosy cheeks and dark eyes.

The artist painted the boy out of doors against a background of dark green trees and grass. He knew that the light suit and sash would look pretty against this dark background.

Isn't this a lovely picture!

If you have seen prints of any other paintings of children, tell about them.

Courtesy of Art Education Press, Inc., New York.

Nancy's Dolls

"Aunt Ruth," said Nancy, "wouldn't you like to see my dolls? They are upstairs."

"Yes, I would," said her aunt.

They went upstairs together.

Aunt Ruth said, "How many dolls have you, Nancy?"

"About a hundred," answered Nancy.

"A hundred!" cried her aunt.

When they reached Nancy's room, Aunt Ruth said, "Oh, they are paper dolls! Now I see why you have so many dolls. And they are all different."

Nancy said, "Mother usually gives me her old magazines. She just gave me one, and I'm cutting out the dolls.

"Look at this girl who is alone! She has on a party dress with a sash. Isn't it a beautiful light blue?"

"Yes, it is," said Aunt Ruth. "It looks nice with her golden hair and rosy cheeks. It matches her blue eyes, too."

Nancy stood two dolls on a low chair. She said, "Here are Tom and Jane. They are wearing their school clothes.

"Look at Jane's dress. Isn't it pretty? It has an all-over design of flowers."

"Tom's clothes look well, too," said Aunt Ruth. "The brown matches his hair and eyes.

"These dolls have the right kind of clothes for school.

"I'm wondering if the little girl with golden hair and rosy cheeks would wear her party dress to school."

"Oh, no!" cried Nancy. "She wouldn't wear a dress like that to school. She is going to meet a friend and go to a party. They will have balloons and a big cake."

Aunt Ruth said, "I hope she will have a good time. But you are right. Party clothes don't make good working clothes."

Nancy showed Aunt Ruth more of her paper dolls.

"Some of them don't have colored clothes," she said. "But I'm going to color them with crayons."

"I will color a doll for you," said Aunt Ruth. "I choose this one.

"I'll color the hat and the coat alike. Clothes that match look well together."

Nancy held up four dolls. "Here is a family," she said. "The mother and the bigger girl are dressed to go down town."

"Aren't they going to take little sister?" asked Aunt Ruth. "She's too small to stay alone."

"She is dressed for play," answered Nancy. "Her brother can stay with her."

Nancy and her aunt colored many of the paper dolls.

After a while Aunt Ruth said, "I like paper dolls, Nancy. Their clothes usually look clean and neat.

"Don't you think that boys and girls look better when their clothes are clean and neat?"

"Oh, yes," said Nancy. "That is why Mother likes to have me hang up my clothes when I take them off.

"She wants me to take good care of them, so that they will always look nice."

At last Aunt Ruth said, "Nancy, you are like the old woman who lived in a shoe.

"She had so many children she didn't know what to do. You have so many dolls you don't know what to do."

"But I love them all," said Nancy.

The Mirror

In Mother's mirror I can see
A little boy that's just like me;
And if my clothes are not just right,
Then he's a sorry looking sight.

But when I try to dress with care,
And wash my face and brush my hair,
The mirror-boy then seems to say,
"Don't you and I look fine today!"

The Picture in Your Mirror

When you look at yourself in a mirror, what do you see?

Do you see a child with clothes that are neat and clean?

Do you see someone who wears party clothes to school or for outdoor play?

The mirror is like a clear picture of yourself. It shows how you look to other people.

When you look in your mirror, do you see a well-dressed child?

These are some things you can do to be well dressed.

Wear colors that look well with your hair and eyes.

Choose colors that look well together.

Always try to keep your clothes clean and neat. Remember to hang up your dresses or suits when you take them off.

Part VII

An Art Exhibit

The children in Miss Pool's room were talking about the good times they were going to have in the summer vacation.

Patty said, "My brother and I are going on the train to visit my cousins in the country."

"Our family usually goes to the beach for part of the summer," said George.

Many of the children planned to have picnics in the park.

While the children were talking about their vacations, some of their mothers came to see Miss Pool.

They talked with her, and suddenly she began to smile.

She turned to the children and said, "Mrs. Bell is going to tell you something interesting."

Mrs. Bell said, "We have planned a surprise for you. An art gallery has sent us some pictures for an art exhibit. We want you to come and see it."

The boys and girls all smiled. Everyone wanted to see the art exhibit.

One child stood up and said, "Thank you, Mrs. Bell. This is a nice surprise. We'll be glad to see the pictures."

When the exhibit was ready, Miss Pool and the children went to see it.

The pictures had been hung in a large room. The children walked around and looked at them.

"What lovely pictures there are!" cried George.

"And they are not all alike," said Betty Ann. "There are pictures of children and pictures of the outdoors."

Ned said, "I see a picture of a vase of flowers."

"There are pictures of many other things, too," said Patty.

Courtesy of The Art Institute of Chicago and The Colonial Art Company, Oklahoma City, Oklahoma.

This is one of the pictures the children saw at the art exhibit.

It shows boys and girls on a beach.

Some of them are playing in the sand, and some are in the water. One girl is modeling something with wet sand.

Farther away you can see some older people. They are having a good time at the beach, too.

See the water where the children are playing. Doesn't it look like a mirror, with its clear, lovely colors?

Most of the children are wearing white clothes.

But when the artist painted the suits and dresses, he put some light colors on them. The blue and violet show the shadows on the clothes.

The artist put some light colors on the sand of the beach, too.

Look at the water in the background of the picture. It has dark blue and violet in it.

Isn't this a lovely picture?

It would be a good picture to choose for a playroom. Its colors would look well with almost any other colors.

Courtesy of The Art Institute of Chicago.

Here is another picture which many of the children liked at the exhibit.

It shows a little girl and her mother out of doors on a clear summer day.

The sun is shining on their rosy cheeks and on their bright hats.

We see the mother and the child in the foreground against the light green branches in the background.

You can see lovely golden colors on the trees. How bright the green leaves are!

Do you see the clear water farther back? It is shining in the sunlight.

The light colors in the background and the dark colors in the foreground look beautiful together.

This picture was painted by a great artist. He was fond of bright sunlight. He liked to paint sunshine on people and on trees and grass and water.

Happy Days

Bob and his brother Paul were watching for Uncle Robert, who stayed with them part of every summer.

"I'm glad Uncle Robert is coming," said Bob. "Vacation is fun when he is here."

Just then a car stopped in front of the house, and their uncle jumped out.

"Hello, boys," he said as they ran to meet him. "I'm glad to see you. We'll have some good times together this vacation."

ART STORIES, BOOK TWO
Curriculum Foundation Series

n art appreciation book for second grade which is at the ame time a valuable addition to the reading program.

ith ART STORIES, every primary teacher -- whether or not he has "artistic ability" or special training -- can ive her pupils functional training in art through mate- ial which the children can read for themselves. And how he children will delight in a book as colorful and in- eresting as this one!

s you examine it, notice these special features:

1. Its <u>readability</u> -- in respect to vocabulary, sentence structure, and ideas. (See pp. 164-5 for vocabulary facts.) In addition to narrative, simple work-type reading is introduced.

2. The richness of content. (See pp. 166-8 for list of art concepts covered.)

3. The suitability and variety of the illustrations; picture-study at the child's level. (See pp. 26, 32, etc.)

4. The many opportunities for correlated activities. (See pp. 13, 15, 16, etc.)

ictures, stories, games, amusing verses, interesting ercise pages, all are utilized to give the child a ading acquaintance with fundamental art concepts and rminology, and to awaken appreciation of beauty in all s forms.

an investment, ART STORIES pays double, for it func- ns in two ways -- as a tool for teaching reading skills as an introduction to a fascinating new field of ap- ciation and knowledge. Make it a part of your second- le program.

ART STORIES, BOOK TWO
Curriculum Foundation Series

An art appreciation book for second grade which is at the same time a valuable addition to the reading program.

With ART STORIES, every primary teacher -- whether or not she has "artistic ability" or special training -- can give her pupils functional training in art through material which the children can read for themselves. And how the children will delight in a book as colorful and interesting as this one!

As you examine it, notice these special features:

1. Its readability -- in respect to vocabulary, sentence structure, and ideas. (See pp. 164-5 for vocabulary facts.) In addition to narrative, simple work-type reading is introduced.

2. The richness of content. (See pp. 165-6 for list of art concepts covered.)

3. The suitability and variety of the illustrations, picture-study at the child's level. (See pp. 23, 32, etc.)

4. The many opportunities for correlated activities. (See pp. 13, 15, 16, etc.)

Pictures, stories, games, amusing verses, interesting exercise pages, all are utilized to give the child a reading acquaintance with fundamental art concepts and terminology, and to awaken appreciation of beauty in all its forms.

As an investment, ART STORIES pays double, for it functions in two ways -- as a tool for teaching reading skills and as an introduction to a fascinating new field of appreciation and knowledge. Make it a part of your second-grade program.

The first thing Uncle Robert and the boys did was to go down town. Uncle Robert wanted to buy something that the boys could enjoy in their vacation.

"I will buy what you choose," he said.

The boys thought of many things. They didn't know which they wanted most.

"Let's look in the store windows as we walk along," said Paul. "Maybe we'll see something we would like."

So they looked in every window.

Suddenly they saw something that made them stop. It was a picture of four boys who were flying kites. The kites were of different colors.

"We haven't had any kites this year," said Paul. "Oh, Uncle Robert, please buy some for us!"

They went to a toy store, and soon the brothers each had a kite. On their way home the boys saw the picture again.

"I like this picture, Uncle Robert," said Bob. "Those boys look like real boys, and they are having fun with their kites. Even the dog seems to be having a fine time."

"The artist wanted you to think they are having a good time," said Uncle Robert. "He called the picture Happy Days.

"Don't you like the colors? Look at the clear blue sky and the light-colored clouds. See how the sunlight shines on the boys and makes shadows on the ground."

The brothers liked the kite picture so well that they often looked at it.

But one day when they went by the window, Happy Days was not in sight.

"The kite picture is gone," said Bob. "Perhaps someone has bought it."

When they got home, Paul went upstairs.

"Bob," he called. "Come here. Please come, too, Uncle Robert."

Courtesy of The Colonial Art Company, Oklahoma City, Oklahoma.

"Oh!" Bob cried. "Someone has hung Happy Days in our room. It must have been Uncle Robert! Thank you, Uncle!"

Bob said, "When we see this picture, we'll remember our happy days with you."

A Statue for a Park

Look at the picture on the next page. It shows a lovely statue.

In this statue the sculptor has shown beautiful curves. Tell where you see curves in it.

Sculptors often like to model squirrels because of their shape. Have you ever tried to model a squirrel yourself?

The sculptor made this statue for a children's park. She thought it would look very pretty with green trees and bright flowers around it.

Statues are often put in parks. When you visit an art gallery, you may see statues there, too.

Perhaps there are some statues in other places in your city, or even in your school. Look for them yourself.

Courtesy of Sylvia Shaw Judson.

Your Art Book

This book has told you about the beauty of the out-of-doors. It has shown you beauty in the work of some great artists.

There are many pictures in this book. Begin at the beginning and look at them again. Which ones do you like best?

You have learned some interesting things about artists and their work.

Can you tell what an architect does?

What does a sculptor do?

What other kinds of work do artists do?

What is an all-over design?

What is a border design?

You have learned of ways to make a room look well. Can you tell about a few of these ways?

What other things have you learned from this book? Perhaps you will want to read it again.

Look for beautiful sights out of doors. Look for beauty in the work that great artists have done, too. Enjoy beauty everywhere you go.

VOCABULARY

The total vocabulary of *Art Stories, Book Two* consists of 654 different words, which have been carefully selected with regard to general and specific reading needs.

The following word list presupposes familiarity with the vocabulary of *The Elson Basic Primer* and *Book One* and *Art Stories, Book One*. *Art Stories, Book Two* introduces 182 additional words, of which 89 (marked with asterisks) appear in *Elson Basic Two*.

9
*secrets
Helen

10
wouldn't
ourselves
*brought
glasses

11
dye
*only

12
*answered
*clean
*turning

13
mixed

14
zinnias
*most
vase
*together

16
*used

17
match
*same

18
game
pencil
*else

19
Ann
*pink

20
*couldn't
*Mr.
*might
*easy

22
*bit

23
*wonder

24
page

25
tan

26
*spring

27
clouds
*near

28
*small
*between
twilight

29
skipping
*rope
*friends

30
*held
*child

33
Raphael
*ever
famous

35
lunch

36
peanuts
suit
bought

37
*napkins

38
lions

39
*I'm
*hand
*smile

40
we'll
*isn't
interesting

41
*few
*enough
space
*didn't

42
scrapbook
*George

43
doesn't
fur

44
*tall
*seem

46
*stood
*afraid
lie
tumbled

47
Peter
fond

49
*tail
fluffy
*aren't
*both

50
straight

51
gallery
52
noticed
*large
54
*can't
copy
copies
prints
55
statues
sculptor
59
different
60
haven't
*proud
61
*remember
63
Paul
puppy
64
*middle
*side
66
architect
plans
*wide
67
*boards
*built
68
*almost
choose
70
bushes
*beside
71
*Ruth
*meet

72
*chimney
73
*won't
74
*men
75
company
76
*alone
78
city
79
*reach
*branches
low
80
enjoy
82
form
shape
office
84
cousin
85
*seven
87
train
*north
88
*upstairs
*suddenly
89
*ice
90
*Mrs.
92
*family
Inness
rosy

94
foreground
96
aunt
97
pool
100
*pieces
*even
101
beauty
*part
*country
103
*been
*move
Ray
104
dining
105
begin
carpet
curtains
106
ceilings
107
*need
usually
110
*package
*cupboard
shelves
112
geese
116
hung
118
*change
*chairs
124
border

131
prince
Carlos
*sent
134
Bonnie's
135
balloon
*march
138
*perhaps
sash
cheeks
140
hundred
143
alike
hope
144
*brother
146
mirror
*sight
147
*yourself
clear
149
exhibit
vacation
*beach
153
*farther
156
Bob
Robert
157
kites
158
*real

INDEX OF ART CONTENT

(References are to pages)

*New in *Book Two*. Subjects not starred were introduced in *Book One*.

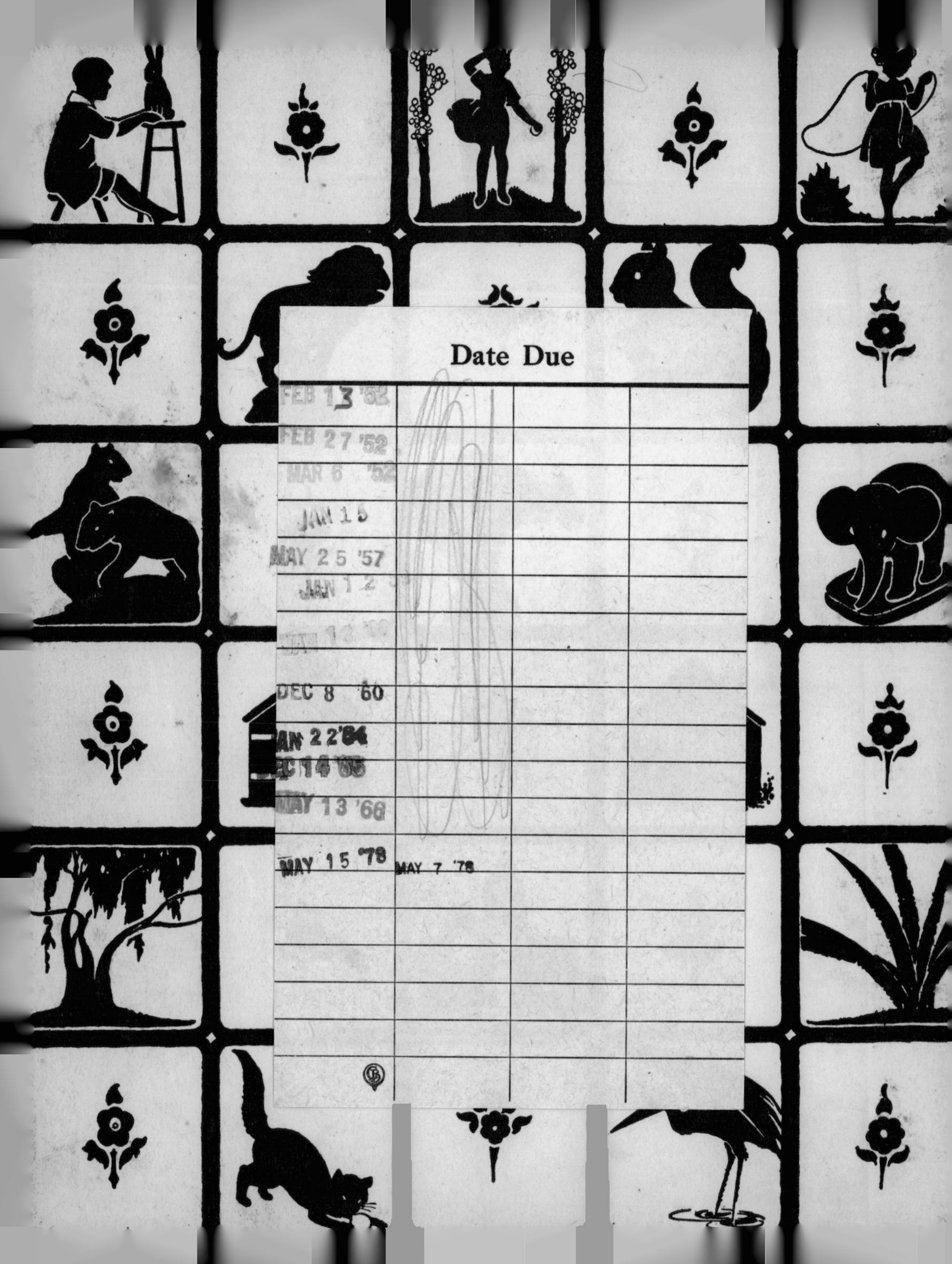